Elephant Problems and Fixes that Fail

The story of a search for new approaches to inter-agency working

John Harris, Pat Gordon, Diane Plamping and Martin Fischer

King's **Fund**

King's Fund Publishing
11–13 Cavendish Square
London W1M 0AN

ISBN 1 85717 232 9 ✓

Available from:

King's Fund Bookshop
11–13 Cavendish Square
London W1M 0AN

Tel: 0171 307 2591
Fax: 0171 307 2801

We would like to dedicate this book to our mothers. It was their stories and rich experiences which gave us confidence that everyone has a story that can contribute to 'making a difference'

Contents

Whole Systems Thinking

WHOLE SYSTEMS THINKING is a series of working papers. They offer insights derived from putting ideas into practice as part of an action research programme – ideas about partnership and whole systems which are now central to the Government's ambitions for sustainable change, regeneration and the development of action zones in employment, education and health.

The papers reflect our experience of developing and applying a new approach to primary health care in cities. Similar issues of partnership and public participation arise elsewhere in the public sector and in the commercial world. We find much in common with people from many different organisations who recognise that, notwithstanding the new political climate, things are not really going to change if we just do 'more of the same'. They, and we, are looking for new ways of working.

WHOLE SYSTEMS THINKING is not a sequential series. It does not matter where you start from and none of the papers offers a complete picture. What we hope you find are thought-provoking ideas, particularly if you are curious about the kind of problems that return to haunt organisations over and over again. Some prove remarkably difficult to influence despite the best efforts of policy-makers and highly motivated people 'on the ground' – homelessness, for instance, and under-achievement in schools, long-term unemployment, 'sink' housing estates, family poverty. Issues like these need effective inter-agency work and consultation with the people who use the services, but even this can seem like a chore rather than part of the solution.

We have long experience of primary health care development in cities and a growing dissatisfaction with change initiatives which both fail to learn the lessons of earlier investment and to deliver desired outcomes. Four years ago we were in the position of developing a new action research programme whose focus was to be the intractable problems we refer to above. These may be recognised as 'wicked' problems. They are ill defined and constantly changing. They are perceived differently by different stakeholders and in trying to tackle them the tendency is to break them into actionable parts, which often turn into projects. We reasoned that if they could be recognised instead as issues for an interconnected system to tackle together, then they may become more tractable.

We chose to shift the focus of our work away from attention to parts and onto 'the whole' and thus to the connections between parts – how things fit together. This led us to explore ideas related to systems dynamics and the 'new science' of complexity. This has resulted in our designing a distinctive set of interventions which link ideas and practice and which we have called whole system working. This is a new development approach which does not offer certainty or guarantee success but it has rekindled our enthusiasm and that of many of the people with whom we are working.

We hope the ideas in these working papers enthuse you too. Because of our roots, many of the examples come from the health sector but we believe the concepts and the practical methods of working whole systems are widely applicable.

Pat Gordon, Diane Plamping, Julian Pratt
King's Fund

Whole Systems Thinking

The Urban Health Partnership is an action research programme on inter-agency working and public participation. The work is in London, Liverpool and Newcastle and North Tyneside, with health agencies and their local partners in housing, local government, commerce, police, transport, voluntary sector and local people.

Further information is available from:

> Pat Gordon, Diane Plamping, Julian Pratt
> Working Whole Systems
> Urban Health Partnership
> King's Fund
> 11–13 Cavendish Square
> London W1M 0AN
>
> Tel: +44(0)171 307 2675
> Fax: +44(0)171 307 2801
> e-mail: wws@dial.pipex.com
> http://dialspace.dial.pipex.com/wws

Editor's Introduction

This interesting and unusual document tells the story of the first two years (1994–96) of the London Health Partnership's primary care development programme. It is told from the point of view of the members of the small operational team who carried out the field-work.

Much of the document was written as the programme was unfolding – only a few parts were written retrospectively. The team are concerned with the truth of their story and intrigued by the inevitable 'tidying up' of history that takes place with hindsight. The implication and nature of writing about events and ideas in retrospect becomes itself a subject for discussion. The editorial task has thus been primarily to make the text clear and readable, but not to change or revise the team's story.

The narrative recounts what they did and why. It traces in particular the interplay of theory and practice, and much of the narrative describes the team's intellectual journey. The team were adventurous and eclectic, excited and inspired by their pursuit of ideas and theories. They devoured anything and everything that seemed relevant. Many of the theories that most interested them were derived from complex and difficult areas of science, including cybernetics, ecology, and chaos and complexity theory. The team grappled with them individually and collectively. Their understandings, interpretations and enthusiasms for different theories developed at varying paces.

The text encapsulates the team's interpretations of these theories as they understood them at particular points in time. This does not always make for an easy read. (Readers may find that the section entitled 'New theories of change in complex adaptive systems' in Chapter 5 is particularly challenging in this respect.) Over time, of course, the team's understandings deepened, broadened, clarified, and changed in the light of experience or new knowledge. They would now write about them differently (and do so, especially when their purpose is to inform and explain to others).

The team admit frankly that often they do not know which came first – the theories or their courses of action. Probably it was sometimes one way, sometimes the other. But they had to come up with something practical – the initiative was about doing things to bring about change, not research. Thus looking for ways to apply the theories to the real world was a large part of their quest.

This story stops after the first two years, so it does not bring us up to date, and does not conclude. For readers who are intrigued and want to know how the ideas and the work have progressed, the team has published a series of working papers under the generic title of Whole Systems Thinking and a book 'Working Whole Systems' is in press.[33,34]

Maggie Jee

Preface

The problem with telling stories

To recount the history of any extended programme of work requires a story that will cover the interrelation of thinking, debate, decisions and actions which together composed the programme. In attempting this task there is an almost overwhelming temptation to tidy up the story. To create logical sequences of developing ideas and actions which make more sense and which reflect better on the managerial capacity, intelligence and insight of the group responsible for the programme. We have, as far as possible, resisted this temptation. However, we are unable to avoid the tendency for hindsight to be a process of construction and making sense. We inevitably reformulate the experience we had then in the light of what we know now and so, no matter how much we want to, we can never tell a really truthful story. It will always come out looking neater than it felt at the time.

One area of unwitting deception which results from this tendency to clean up the story is particularly important. It relates to the interplay of action and theory. We need to make it clear that, while we believe that the theory described here is relevant to the domain of interest, we became aware of this theory as we went along. We are sometimes able to describe what happened in terms of theory but we are not pretending that the theory necessarily informed our actions. Sometimes it did, and other times we were quite unaware of it or of its importance. Now, after the event, we simply cannot, for the most part, remember the knowledge and the conversations which led to specific decisions.

Please keep this in mind when you read this. We hope that you will learn from our experience. We hope that you will be able to deploy the theory and methods described in this material more explicitly and consciously than we often did. We also hope that you will recognise that the capacity to act is not dependent on a comprehensive set of coherent insights. If it were, no one would dare to act in new ways, and progress and development would never be achieved.

Chapter 1

The background to the London Health Partnership

The state of London's health services in the early 1990s

Like most capital cities, London has extremes of wealth and poverty, immense racial and cultural diversity, growing numbers of elderly people without family support, people who are inadequately housed or homeless, as well as many thousands of people who travel daily to work or to seek work there. These factors have always posed challenges for the NHS and never more so than in the early 1990s, when our health care system was being reshaped by powerful social, demographic and economic pressures.

Throughout the industrialised world, health systems are having to respond to changing patters of need – for many conditions, the long-term management of chronic ill health has become as relevant as the treatment of its acute episodes. Technological changes mean that much of the care that is traditionally given in out-patient departments, hospital beds, or accident departments can potentially be delivered much closer to people's homes. These changes are also being brought about by numerous user groups who have demanded and won changes to health care delivery. Increasingly, there is a preference from users for community-based services. The hospital of the future is likely to be very different from that of today.

Primary care, that is health care outside hospitals, is one of the key building blocks of the future. In our system, general practice is considered the cornerstone of primary care. Interest in the development of general practice in cities is long-standing. Over many years national incentives for developing general practice – which have worked well in other settings – have worked erratically or not at all in cities. In London in particular 'the problem' of inner city primary care is well rehearsed and has received particular attention since the publication of the Acheson Report in 1981[1]. The situation remains one of great variation and patchy development, with the best and the worst in general practice only streets apart.

During the 1980s and 90s the King's Fund, as a foundation for London and the health of Londoners, invested in the development of primary care services. The Fund's Primary Health Care Group took a wider view of primary care to include the network of community-based services which work with and through general practice. In much the same way as the development of general practice is influenced by the proximity of large teaching hospitals, so the development of community health services is influenced by the pattern of care provided by general practice. Much has been learned from demonstration projects about what constitutes appropriate and valued primary care in the city[2]. It is clear that there have been substantial improvements and yet these have not kept pace with much of the rest of the country. With more than a decade of experience, the Fund was beginning to look for a new development approach. Were there new ways in which charitable foundations could effectively deploy their resources to support those trying to bring about change?

A new development programme for London's primary care services

In 1992 the Government accepted in principle that London's hospitals should be 'rationalised' onto fewer sites and, at the same time, there should be major investment in the capital's primary care services, after many years of neglect. The rationale of a three-point development programme was accepted in order to:

- improve the basics of primary care and bring core services to a standard common elsewhere
- develop more flexible primary care services to meet the needs of the diverse groups of people who live and work in London
- achieve a shift in the balance of care from hospitals to community-based services.

By 1993 the London Implementation Group (LIG) had been set up to carry through a major reform programme based on the Department of Health's publication, Making London Better[3]. Much of inner London had been designated a London Initiative Zone for the purposes of primary care development. Some £170m capital investment was to be provided over the next six years. A further £7.5m was to be made available over three years for voluntary sector providers of community-based services. (It is interesting to compare these sums made available for primary care development with the amounts going into the transitional funds to support London's Hospitals during the same period: £6 million per annum.)[4]

An investment fund for London

In addition, the Government was considering putting up £1m for a 'challenge fund' for innovative projects that cut across traditional boundaries, and which they hoped would attract the private sector. The King's Fund explored the idea with other charitable foundations. LIG money was earmarked for improving the basics, thus there was an opportunity to reconsider the scope and uses for charitable funds. There was little interest, however, in the idea of 'challenge' or 'competition' and much scepticism about 'doing the Government's business'.

But there was interest in the idea of an investment fund or venture capital for a programme of work which would add up to more than the many good projects which individual foundations could support at any time. One of the trusts expressed their interest in joining forces with the King's Fund because of its 'potential to act as a reverberating chamber'.

Consultation: the purpose of an investment fund

The King's Fund decided to consult widely on what an investment fund might be used for. We commissioned a 'quick and dirty' study of the views of GPs and held three consultation days with people from health and social care and the voluntary sector. We circulated widely what we called a 'preliminary paper' containing our ideas on how an investment fund for primary care development in London might work. In the preliminary paper we proposed concentrating on:

- the positive area of innovation at the boundaries between hospitals and community-based care

- ideas that in some way break the mould of established assumptions about primary and secondary care to provide better services for Londoners. A key point is that development would be needed across the health-care system as a whole: changes in hospital-based services imply changes in primary and community health services, and vice versa. This in turn means that development can start at either end of the service: in hospital or in the community.

We used the consultation days to seek views on the content and focus for investment: how the fund could be distinctive but complementary to other investments, and the criteria for funding. We asked participants to address four questions relating to development capacity within their own organisations:

- If my organisation was investing what would it spend money on?
- Where do ideas come from in my organisation (and where are the gaps)?
- What helps and/or hinders translating ideas into action in my organisation?
- How would an investor spot a good bet?

We had several clear messages from these initial consultations.

First, what was wanted was help with the 'elephant problems' of providing services in London – those problems which seem enormous and immovable, which have been around for a long time, and which involve different agencies each with a view of the parts but none of the whole. Examples given were services for mentally ill people and for vulnerable elderly people.

Secondly, we were made to understand that a competitive bidding process for non-recurrent monies is a distraction rather than a help, especially during periods of major change.

Thirdly, there was agreement that this fund should be used *distinctively*. What this meant was not entirely clear but people talked of not picking up projects that LIG could fund, of funding 'difficult boundaries' and overlaps between agencies, and of using it as 'learning money'.

Formation of the London Health Partnership

In June 1994 the London Health Partnership (LHP) was formed as an alliance of charitable foundations, business interests and government, with Liam Strong, Chief Executive of Sears plc, as its Chairman. The King's Fund set up a small group to be responsible for the operational and financial management of the programme, and a Steering Group (or Board), made up of representatives from the sponsoring organisations, to generally oversee the programme. In addition, The Baring Foundation and the King's Fund agreed to combine forces to work in parallel on urban primary care in Tyneside and Merseyside. This would provide an important opportunity to compare London and other cities.

As a result of the extended consultation exercise the LHP Board decided to focus on services for vulnerable elderly people, and to adopt a phased work process in order to judge how best to use its resources to bring about lasting change. We expressed our intentions as 'learning how to do things differently to add value to the many good projects which foundations can choose to support at any time, and to the Government's current investment in improving the basics of primary care'.

Chapter 2

The early stages of the LHP – guiding principles

Beginning with primary care

Our starting point was the enhancement of primary care in London. We always defined primary care broadly (preferring to use the term 'primary *health* care'), and we did not hold the view that primary care is synonymous with general practice. Over time, as we shall describe, we moved still further, beyond the boundary of health care services. The following attempts to capture the essence of our approach at this time:

> *Primary care is a network of community-based health services that covers prevention of ill health, treatment of acute and chronic illness, rehabilitation, support at home for patients who are frail, elderly, disabled or acutely or chronically ill, and terminal care. In our system, general practice is generally considered to be the bedrock of primary care.*

As a whole primary care is much less visible and less well understood than hospital care. Yet, these are the services that make it possible in this country to manage 90 per cent of care outside hospitals, to limit patients' length of stay in hospital and discharge them safely, and to maintain at home people who do not want to be institutionalised.

Finding a Focus: the well-being of older people

At the same time as we were widening the boundary of primary care we were focusing in on services of relevance to the well-being of older people. This group was chosen for three reasons. We knew from epidemiological and other evidence that a high proportion of older people

- have multiple health needs and a high degree of chronic ill health
- live alone and are relatively poor
- use a wide range of agencies and voluntary organisations.

Developing Guiding Principles

From the beginning, the LHP recognised that while it had a significant sum of money at its disposal, this money was very small in relation to the combined budgets of the statutory agencies and voluntary organisations whose services it hoped to influence. The operational group had many discussions about how this money should be spent. We formulated a number of guiding principles derived from our consultation and our sense that 'this was what people wanted', to help determine the methods of working and the issues to be addressed.

The LHP's work would be:

- **Programmatic.** The work would form a coherent programme over a period of three to five years, not a series of discrete and unrelated interventions.

- **Distinctive.** This was not because novelty was itself desirable but because the LHP provided an opportunity to explore approaches to working which other agencies were generally unable or unwilling to adopt. We were interested in innovation only to the extent that this meant the effective implementation of ideas. We were not in the business of inventing new ideas for their own sake.

In keeping with the findings from the consultation, we were also seeking new and distinctive ways in which charitable foundations could most effectively deploy their resources. And, as a legacy from the King's Fund London Commission, we were determined to involve Londoners in any solutions for London's health services.

The issues to be addressed would be:

- **Intractable.** The LHP believed that current organisations and services required support, and new ways to help define and address longstanding problems. If problems had proved to be intractable then old solutions had, by definition, proved inadequate. New approaches were required.

- **'Elephant problems'.** We did not look at elephants as just large, immovable objects that have been around for a long time. We took an alternative idea from the Sufi tale of the blind men examining the elephant who each came to a different conclusion about the nature of the beast. We hypothesised that the intractable problems in which we were interested would be interpreted in different ways by different stakeholders and that the difficulties in reconciling these perspectives would contribute to their intractability.

- **At the Boundaries.** The OG knew from experience that many dysfunctional aspects of health and social services were attributable to problems at the boundaries of services, organisations or professional groups. This finding was indeed such a common experience in our work that we jokingly referred to ourselves as 'boundroids'.[5]

Boundary problems are often experienced by service users as poor coordination between departments and services. One response to this has been the attempt to create 'seamless' services. But 'seamlessness' has proved difficult to put into practice, and we believe it is a misguided approach. We were not interested in the removal of seams but in recognising them, and making them explicit. We prefer to go for something not seamless and baggy but finely stitched and well tailored – a service that fits the needs of the users.

Chapter 3

The diagnostic phase of the LHP's work & exploring systems theories

The nature of diagnosis

The LHP's role was to enhance primary health care for older people by using its financial and human resources to address intractable problems. We were thus firmly in the paradigm of problem definition and resolution. Diagnosis, as part of that process, assumes that:

- problems exist
- processes can be deployed by which these problems are recognised and described
- separate processes can be defined for addressing the problem.

The LHP operational group are experienced 'process' consultants. We were thus alert to avoiding some of the pitfalls in classic doctor-patient models of consultation and diagnosis. These models and their shortcomings have been well described elsewhere[6]. A successful diagnosis in the classic model depends on four factors:

- whether the client/organisation consulting the 'doctor' has accurately identified which group or department ('patient') is sick
- whether the 'patient' will reveal accurate information
- whether the 'patient' will accept and believe the diagnosis that the 'doctor' arrives at
- whether the 'patient' will accept the prescription, that is, do what the 'doctor' recommends.

We knew we were dealing with complex problems involving a range of stakeholders and were therefore aware that it was very unlikely that the above four requirements for success would be achieved. We knew that we would need to work *with* stakeholders to enable us jointly to diagnose the problems and design the solutions.

We designed two kinds of diagnostic events to involve stakeholders: *large scale consultations* and *systems mapping*. They are described in this chapter. They were well worth doing and were valued both by us and the participants. However, they failed to achieve their original intended purpose. They did not result in the articulation of neatly bounded problems or the identification of viable solutions. The nature of the insights gained was very different from what we had expected and proved invaluable in thinking through subsequent approaches. These insights are outlined later in the chapter.

At the same time as these diagnostic efforts were proceeding, we were actively seeking theories of relevance to the understanding of complex systems and to intervening purposefully in them. Our explorations, and our interpretations of the theories we found useful, are also included in this chapter.

Diagnostic events: Large scale consultation

Why large scale consultation?

Having decided that the work of the LHP would focus on services for older people, the operational group determined to start defining the problems with their help. We had already started this process informally by talking with and about our own mothers. During the course of this programme we became intimately acquainted with the well-being of each other's mothers and with their experiences of health and social services.

Common sense dictated that it would be helpful to hear, first-hand, about older people's experience of services, but there were a number of deeper reasons why we considered that their perspective would be essential. The work of Richard Normann[7] was hugely influential in developing our ideas on involving service users (set out below), and shaping our subsequent practice. He writes lucidly about the integration of services around the individual user, users as co-producers of services, and the nature of value and quality in the service sector.

Users as the focus of multiple services

As already stated, older people, as a group, tend to make more use of services and use a wider variety of those services than other groups. They are thus the centre of a constellation of care providers who are required to integrate their services to varying degrees. The extent to which these services effectively integrate or overlap and duplicate or fail to comprehensively address needs is best assessed by the recipients of those services. **The only individual with a full picture of the impact of the relationship between care providers is the service user.**

Perceptions of quality

Many older people suffer from chronic illnesses and conditions. Treatment involves management and care, rather than cure. Appropriate interventions can result in them getting worse more slowly and maintaining their independence for longer. Quantitative measures of quality, such as may be applied to many technical interventions in acute hospitals, are very difficult to apply. As enhancing well-being is the aim, the subjective opinion of the service user should be a key measure by which quality is assessed. Such opinions are extremely difficult for management to elicit. **The quality of care is created in the exchanges between the service provider and the user (often in the user's home) and the user is best placed to evaluate them.**

Co-production of services

Older people living in the community are not the passive recipients of services from professional groups. They have the capacity to be involved in the delivery of their own care and the role of professionals is often to help them realise this potential. **In addition to functioning as co-providers, older people also have the potential (less frequently used by provider organisations) to become involved in the service design process.**

Empowering older people

These early diagnostic events were one mechanism by which the LHP attempted to take a fresh approach to empowering older people. Power can be defined as the ability to put things on the agenda, take them off the agenda or make things happen[8]. **These diagnostic events were an early opportunity to make elders equal partners in setting the agenda, not simply being asked to comment on other people's concerns or pre-digested solutions.**

What happened at the Large scale consultation events

Between 90 and 120 older people participated in each event, many of whom were disabled. Each event lasted a day, and most of the activity took place in small, facilitated, groups of eight to ten people. The events were facilitated overall by the operational group, but group facilitators were volunteers drawn from a range of agencies. These volunteers were often inexperienced as facilitators but were required only to ensure that everyone in their group felt that they had been heard, to record the main points from the discussion on to a flip chart, and to keep time. This model of facilitation can be described as 'public listening'.

In conducting the large scale consultations we attempted to get some answers (not *the* answer) to the following questions.

- What issues, relating to services which influence their well-being, are most widespread and significant for older people themselves?
- How are these issues experienced?
- What ideas do the users themselves have about the ways in which services could be improved?
- Which of these issues look most promising as candidates for intervention by the LHP?
- To what extent do these issues conform to our idea of 'intractable problems' ?

The morning sessions were devoted to personal biographies of experiences of health and social care services. Participants were asked to speak about themselves or someone known to them personally rather than in the abstract or on behalf of any organisation with which they might be associated. During the afternoon sessions new groupings of participants were asked to address ways in which they felt services could be improved, to address problems raised by the biographies or, in some cases, how they might further enhance existing good services.

The idea of 'public listening' was reinforced throughout the day by the videoing of the event and the use of 'group graphics' techniques[9] to capture some of the main themes. These graphics were created in 'real time', displayed, and discussed. An illustrator worked throughout the day capturing what he heard as the discussions were proceeding on large sheets of paper on the walls.

There was no attempt to abstract themes during plenary sessions. Participants were aware from their invitations that this was a consultative event and that they were giving their time. This was reinforced during the event by the main facilitators from the LHP.

Many participants declared, very publicly, that they had enjoyed the day and found it stimulating. We believe that this enthusiasm was due to the tight organisation of the event, and the full use that was made of the time with the older people. As one participant commented, they 'felt usefully exploited'. This was in sharp contrast to many of the biographical stories of services scheduled for the logistical efficiency of service providers rather than convenience of users, which demonstrated a complete indifference to the time of older people.

All of us were struck by two key characteristics of the older people with whom we worked. They were a very mixed group about whom it was very difficult to generalise. And they were a very 'feisty' bunch: the one generalisation it seemed safe to make was that they demonstrated a high level of assertiveness and a strong desire for autonomy.

Feedback on the principal findings of the event was provided in an interim Progress Report for all participants (Appendix I).

Exploring and developing our ideas about systems

In the next phase of the diagnostic process we intended to create models of the systems of care which served older people. We hoped that these models would reveal some of the underlying reasons for the inadequacy of services which had been highlighted in the large scale consultation exercises. We further hoped that the models would give clues about the nature of the interventions which may improve services.

What do we mean by 'systems'?

Like any work group which achieves effective team working, we shared a developing set of ideas and a language to describe what we were doing. This distinctive use of language facilitated our own internal communication but often presented a barrier when talking about our ideas to the outside world with whom we hoped to collaborate. Some words recurred so frequently in our conversations that we even started to irritate ourselves with their repetition. At one point we thought about setting up a 'swear box' to limit our dependence on this vocabulary. First on the list of words to be targeted was 'systems'.

We realised that to get beyond irritation, and to improve communication with others, we had to be clearer and more consistent about what we meant by 'system'. To help us, we needed to delve into the vast literature on systems, systems thinking and systems analysis.

Our exploration of systems thinking is a prime example of the parallel development of our theoretical understanding and our practice. Sometimes theory informed practice, but generally the theory proved more useful in analysing and providing insight into what had happened after the event. We are not going to try to distil the literature for this paper, but our actions at this time were mainly informed by a handful concepts which we believe are worth outlining.

Inter-relatedness of parts and emergence

In the introduction to his book *Systems Thinking, Systems Practice*, Peter Checkland[10] writes:

> *The central concept 'system' embodies the idea of a set of elements connected together to form a whole, this showing properties which are properties of the whole rather than properties of its component parts. (The taste of water for example is a property of the substance water not of the hydrogen and oxygen which combine to form it.) Systems thinking then makes conscious use of the particular concept of wholeness captured in the word 'system', to order our thoughts. 'Systems practice' then implies using the product of this thinking to initiate and guide actions we take in the world.*

This short passage embodies two key concepts: the **interrelationship of parts** and the quality of **emergence**. 'Emergence' refers to the phenomenon that at certain levels of complexity properties emerge which are not explicable in terms of lower levels. Water's taste or wetness is not explicable by even the most exhaustive analysis of its separate constituents. No amount of chemical analysis will explain the sensation you feel when eating your favourite chocolates.

Information, feedback and co-evolution

Jay Forrester[11] has been among the most influential systems thinkers and is the founder of a systems modelling technique known as 'systems dynamics'. The following passage is quoted by Ralph Stacey in his book, Management & Organisational Dynamics[12]:

Systems of information feedback control are fundamental to all life and human endeavour, from the slow pace of biological evolution to the launching of the latest satellite. A feedback control system exists whenever the environment causes a decision which in turn affects the environment.

In human interactions and organisations, behaviour is influenced by information feedback. In the same way, behaviour influences the environment in which the person or organisation operates. The changing environment imposes new influences which require different human responses. The cyclical interplay between the behaviour of the person or organisation and their environment means that they co-evolve together.

Cause and effect in complex systems

Complex systems are characterised by non-linear relationships (i.e. change in A does not result in corresponding, proportional change in B), with positive feedback (tending to reinforce behaviour) and negative feedback (tending to dampen-down behaviour). Complex systems are also characterised by an abundance of interconnected parts. In such systems it is often very difficult to track cause-and-effect relationships – there are so many, and it is often impossible to determine what are causes and what are effects (the term 'tightly-coupled' is sometimes applied to systems in which there is an interplay between many causes and many effects). Furthermore, cause and effect tend to be separated in space and time. Concurrent changes can easily be interpreted as being of a causal nature which may hide other possible, but more obscure, causal connections. Mistaken beliefs about cause may mean that 'obvious solutions' are inappropriate. In dynamic, complex systems causal relationships and connections are often counterintuitive and may have unexpected consequences.

Senge[13], also quoted in Stacey[12], has observed:

The art of systems thinking lies in being able to recognise increasingly dynamical, complex and subtle structures ... amid the wealth of details, pressures and cross currents that attend all real management settings. In fact, the essence of mastering systems thinking as a management discipline lies in seeing patterns where others see only events and forces to react to.

Sensitivity and resistance to change in complex systems

Complex systems tend to contain a few critical pressure points and interventions at these points will result in significant change. However, these points are extremely difficult to identify. Attempts to change complex systems by interventions in the wrong places usually result in compensatory actions by the system to maintain stability and the status quo.

Most of us will have experience of major interventions and change efforts which make little substantive difference and, conversely, small interventions which appear to have considerable impact.

Applying systems concepts to our work: the pragmatic LHP view

At this point in the development of our systems thinking, we took a very simple view. We believed that it would be useful to think of older people and the assortment of care services and organisations which supported them as a system. The system would have a rather fuzzy geographical boundary corresponding roughly to the operational limits of the agencies involved and to the areas in which the older people lived, who were served by those agencies. If we thought of this grouping as a system, and analysed it using the key concepts we had acquired, there were profound implications for the kinds of interventions that would make these services better. We now felt that we had some theoretical backing in support of our hunch that it was connections at the boundaries that were important. We realised we were on the right lines, and were optimistic about the possibility of finding critical pressure points to which LHP resources could be applied to bring about systems transformation.

It is worth emphasising that these systems ideas are not simply interesting academic devices, nor are they only relevant in the fields of health and social care. The chairman of the LHP is Liam Strong, who is also the Chief Executive of Sears plc, the largest retailer in the UK*. He has been consciously applying systems thinking to address a wide range of issues affecting Sears and its relationship to its external environment. For example, what is the interrelationship of transport services and the viability of Sears retail outlets? What is the relationship between Sears and its neighbours in the high street? How can Sears contribute to the economic regeneration of the areas in which it is a stakeholder?

Our continued flirtation with systems dynamics

As our exploration of systems theories deepened, some of us became particularly interested in the application of Jay Forrester's ideas[11]. He has developed a systems dynamics approach to modelling complex human systems.

His method uses a notation of arrows and feedback loops to create models which have the power to explain a number of well-recognised patterns (or archetypes) which many of us have seen in real world organisations. It also highlights possible intervention points which may enable the system to improve. Examples of three patterns follow[14,13].

'Fixes that fail'

In a 'fixes that fail' archetype a problem symptom cries out for resolution. A solution is quickly implemented that alleviates the symptom, but the unintended consequences of the 'fix' exacerbate the problem. Over time the problem symptom returns to its previous level or becomes worse.

'Shifting the burden'

In a 'shifting the burden' archetype, a problem is solved by applying a symptomatic solution which diverts attention away from more fundamental solutions. In extreme cases the side effects of the solution can overwhelm the original problem symptom.

'Tragedy of the commons'

In a 'tragedy of the commons' archetype, each person pursues actions which are individually beneficial. If the amount of activity grows too great for the system to support, however, the

---

* In 1998 Strong left Sears PLC and became CEO of WorldCom International.

commons become overloaded and everyone experiences diminishing benefits. ('All for one and none for all')

Mental maps

A further key concept from systems dynamics to which we returned frequently was the idea of 'mental maps'. Players in a system each hold their own perspective of the system. The mental maps which they construct are partial and biased. In the language of Margaret Wheatley[15], '*the system often fails to recognise itself as a system or to have access to itself*'.

As we explored these ideas we told ourselves stories to illuminate the concepts. The stories were drawn from our personal experience and also from some of the situations and problems that had been thrown up by the consultation events. They are included in the following boxes.

Box 1   Mental Maps: the system does not have access to itself

'The system doesn't have access to itself', is one of our favourite pieces of jargon. This concept feels powerful to us because we have seen it demonstrated. Even well-connected people can 'discover' important functions or people in their work environment that they didn't know existed, or realise the significance/interconnectedness of something they had previously failed to see as part of 'their system'. We have seen over and over again, for example, the ready acceptance of transport as vitally important to the smooth operating of the health care system, but a repeated failure to invite transport representatives into systems-wide discussions.

There are issues arising all the time in the health service which appear mysterious either because of incorrect attributions of cause and effect, or because of insufficient evidence to support the usual causal explanation.

To illustrate the first case let's take a (true) example which involved one of the operational group. The chairs of local hospital trusts were meeting to discuss a report which showed an increase in the numbers of operations cancelled. The data presented showed a small decrease in elective surgery, some decrease in emergency admissions, and an increase in daycase work. The chairs believed the cancellation rate was caused by an increase in emergency admissions and continued to do so *even after the data was presented*. The regional officer collected extra data during the course of the meeting to show there was no correlation between an increase in cancellations and emergency admissions. Collapse of stout party? No, just disbelief of the data.

As an example of the second case (insufficient information/evidence) let's take an issue facing an elderly care division in a community trust. Their figures showed a decrease in the use of continuing care beds – only 80% occupancy at a time when there was supposed to be a huge shortage of such beds.

In spite of the figures the elderly care division were convinced that they in fact needed *more* beds. They admitted that they did not know why their figures showed a decline, and they did not know what the pattern of bed use was. Was the decline caused by GPs changing their behaviour because of difficulties in admitting some time ago? Were there older people who needed this type of care but were just not getting it? Had the care programmes instituted by the local authority 'kicked in'? It was clear that the board did not have access to information within the system in which it operated. Needless to say this lack of information did not modify the division's conviction that they needed more beds – this assertion had the ring of eternal truth in their minds!

Box 2 Shifting the Burden – attention to symptoms and not causes

NHS workforce planning is brilliant example of dealing with symptoms not causes. For years there has been huge wastage in nursing training. Rather than do something about the wastage – there are some good ideas about factors which contribute to the drop-out rate – we just train the number we need plus the predicted wastage. (Editorial Note: In 1998 this is beginning to change.)

Why do we avoid dealing with the causes? It may be because they arise from the organisation of the work in the ward/hospital as well as the quality of the training course. One of the key elements of the problem is the nature of the hierarchy, which precludes the students' voice being heard. In this case the system probably 'knows' it is a system but it does not have access to itself. The sources of information which could illuminate the solution are many and held by different people. They probably all have different views about causes. It would need the whole system to agree issues and solutions.

Box 3 Fixes that fail: all you need is good people

There are many creative people working in complex and challenging situations who successfully influence services for people. They are often highly internally motivated and make a difference while they are in their job. This may be sufficient to sustain them but they often 'burn out' and leave. It is not uncommon for the service they have developed to decay rapidly once they have departed.

A chair of a NHS trust told us there is no problem with working across boundaries you just need good people. She really means exceptional people and by definition such people are the exception. In the past we have talked of these special people as 'boundroids'. By seeking them out and letting them individually solve problems, the system often fails to learn anything. The old rules and procedures continue to operate, and innovation may well not persist. This is an issue of attribution of cause which sees individual rather than systems solutions. There is often an attempt to generalise success criteria at one level to the next, i.e. motivation aids the individual innovator so we must 'motivate' the rest of the work force. In systems thinking 'transformations' at one level do not necessarily operate at other levels.

Box 4 Why systems approaches are helpful for Elephant problems

Elephant problems are issues which look different depending on your vantage point. The debate about emergency care typifies an elephant problem and demonstrates the difficulty of dealing with such issues if you don't take a systems approach. Let's start with the use of language. What is emergency care? Is it

- post-accident care – which implies unexpected, but can range in seriousness from minor injury (sprains and cuts, etc.) to major trauma (RTAs)
- out-of-hours care – people may well have the same care needs as at other times, but the surgery or clinic is closed
- urgent care – which is linked to patient perceptions and knowledge and level of anxiety. Does a child sick at night have meningitis or not?
- serious acute conditions – where delay will damage prognosis (e.g. treatment of heart attacks)?

> ### Box 4   Why systems approaches are helpful for Elephant problems (*cont.*)
>
> They all require risk assessment, but what else do they have in common?
>
> These elephant problems often seem intractable and we would contend that this is to do with the need for a systems approach rather than a single-agency or single-profession intervention. There are usually no mechanisms for bringing all perspectives together 'to find what the system wants to happen'.

Diagnostic events: systems mapping

Applying theory to practice

Despite the elegance and explanatory power of the systems dynamics models we decided not to use them in our investigation of systems of care for older people. This was for two reasons:

- Using the models with organisations is a technical virtuoso performance. We were simply not expert enough in the technique.

- We wanted to be able to model systems with a wide range of personnel from care organisations, and with users. We needed a modelling technique which would be easy for everyone in such groups to grasp. We wanted the technique to aid communication, not get in the way.

However, we did hope to discover some dysfunctional archetypes within health and social service systems and identify possible interventions for systems improvement. While retaining an interest in systems dynamics, and using the language of the archetypes such as those described above, we intended to use a different modelling approach which we had to invent for ourselves .

The systems we worked with

To develop our modelling method we located and worked with a number of systems at different geographical scales, working with different combinations of personnel and users to carry out the analysis. We worked with:

- a neighbourhood – which included elderly people and their carers together with their local voluntary groups and professionals: a GP, district nurse, health visitor, and occupational therapists.

- a large general practice – which as well as the general practice staff and patients included nurses from the community trust, the discharge planner from the local hospital, a local pharmacist and staff from a 'home from hospital' private agency.

- two NHS localities in a city – which covered several general practices and included locality managers and front line staff, local voluntary agencies and elderly people

- two boroughs – one included managers from the hospital and community health services, development managers from the health authorities, the local authority community care planner, the local voluntary organisations coordinator, and service users. In the other we worked with senior executives from the local authority, social services, environmental health and housing, the health commission, the community health services trust, the mental health trust, the local hospital, and a GP, and community groups.

- a city – where we worked with a group of senior managers, including chief executives, similar to the second borough.

The LHP systems mapping approach

The method we finally used allowed us to work with groups of up to 25 people to examine how their systems functioned. As with the earlier large scale consultation exercises, group graphics techniques proved to be a crucial aspect of the method. It enabled participants to hold and grapple with the full complexity of their system and did not force them to make generalisations or simplify cases and examples.

We used a diagramming technique[9] in which one person (usually an artist) captures the groups' discussions through diagrams (approximately 20ft x 4 ft) which narrate the stories of typical service users. Group participants are encouraged to make the stories as rich and detailed as possible to include the services of all the organisations present. People become immersed in these stories and contribute enthusiastically, drawn in by the power of the narrative unfolding on the wall. The technique can be revelatory as participants discover new ways of understanding their system. Most find they acquire

- a much better understanding of the complexity of the system of which they are a part
- an ability to critically scrutinise their previous assumptions about the way their system works (for example, after the exercise people could see how their initial assumptions about 'the problem' and 'the solution' were wrong or inadequate)
- an awareness of a discrepancy between what is supposed to happen ('what the rules say') and what actually happens (what works by custom and practice)
- an understanding of the ways in which the system shifts the problem from one organisation, role, profession or individual to another
- the ways in which unintended and often dysfunctional consequences emerge over time.

We believe that there was also great value to the participants from working together in mixed groups including health, social and voluntary agencies, simultaneously sharing and learning. A tremendous buzz was generated at all events, particularly when groups arrived collectively at a revelatory insight. Such exciting moments included the discovery of:

- the absence of effective feedback loops in organisations and across the system – for example the recognition that the profound knowledge of field staff is rarely, if ever, fed back to managers
- the significance of 'inadmissible evidence' – that is, the recognition that the system cannot make use of information about how things are really done, as opposed to how they are officially done, because such 'inadmissible evidence' is neither recorded nor acknowledged
- people's limited knowledge and understanding of other parts of the system – typified in the frequent stories of 'the left hand not knowing what the right was doing'
- the idiosyncratic and limited notions held by most people about the nature of 'solutions'.

These sessions were particularly useful when they involved the chief executives of the service agencies. The insights they developed made them see the system of which they were a part more clearly and made them want to be involved in subsequent processes aimed at generating these insights on a much larger scale.

Findings from our Diagnostic Events

As discussed earlier, the diagnostic process, as originally conceived, failed – it did not provide us with discrete problems to try to solve collaboratively. However, the nature of the insights gained was very powerful. We believe that these, or similar, methods can be powerful diagnostic tools to precede the development/implementation of full-scale systems interventions. In addition to the specific issues listed in the Progress Report of December 1994 (Appendix I), we discovered:

- Problems experienced by older people often do not translate into neatly packaged sets of issues directly reflected in dysfunctions in service provision. The problems they experience are often systemic and emergent in nature (for example difficult physical access, poor availability of information, or widespread experience of ageism).

- Paradoxically, the most complicated cases are often the best handled. The care system seems to be able to integrate and customise its service in complex cases. This does not happen in the majority of cases, which are much simpler.

- The demands of older people are extremely modest. The fears of service providers that they will be overwhelmed with demands if they consult openly with older people, and respond to their agenda, seem to be unwarranted.

- Where integration and customisation of services does occur, it seems to happen as a result of a constant exchange of informal and semi-formal communication between conscientious and well meaning front line staff. To prompt significant service redesign the insights of front line staff and users would have to be given managerial impetus.

- It seems very difficult to provide gradual and finely modulated responses to slowly progressing health or social needs. There appears to be an inexorable tendency to rapidly escalate responses, pushing problems up the chain to 'higher', more specialised, interventionist and expensive professionals and services.

- The well-being of older people is significantly influenced by a range of agencies and individuals extending well beyond the boundaries of formal health and social care agencies.

These findings made us recognise that we needed to find new kinds of solutions. Experts in these kinds of problems did not exist. Even if they did exist, they would be unable to persuade those who needed to change their behaviours and redesign their services to do so. These problems would not bend before purely rational analysis. The specific stakeholders involved in any local system needed to understand their interrelationship and to work together to change the ways in which care was provided. The kinds of insights available to the LHP and the participants in the diagnostic processes need to be gained and shared by all the relevant stakeholders in local systems.

The relationship of diagnosis to action

Back at the beginning we had started with a simple notion of a problem, and were familiar with theories to support our unsophisticated view. We were expecting neatly defined problems that would reveal a gap between actual and desired states that we would (collectively) try to close. Problems resolved. Our experience of the consultation and diagnostic phase disabused us of these notions, once and for all. We found no gaps, but complex messes of problems.

We realised we needed to understand more about the nature of different kinds of problems, particularly complicated problems in organisational and 'systems' contexts. We also needed to investigate the relationship between the complexity of a problem, and the possible ways in which we might try to effect change.

This section details our journey, and where it left us at the point in the programme where we needed to turn from diagnosis to action. We outline theories that interested or helped us and also draw on our own experience to highlight some of the problem-diagnosing-solving issues we were struggling with.

What is a problem?

Simple problems

At its simplest a problem can be defined as a gap between what is and what should be. If what is and what is desired are identical then no problem exists. A simple problem-solving model has been described by Van Gundy[16]. According to Van Gundy the following pre-conditions are necessary in order to begin the problem-solving process:

- the existence of a gap between what is and what should be
- an awareness that a gap exists
- the motivation to decrease the gap
- an ability to measure the size of the gap
- the availability of the abilities and resource required to close the gap.

When we embarked on the two kinds of diagnostic processes described earlier, we assumed the existence of a gap and hoped to:

- use the large scale consultations to describe the gap and start to generate the motivation in ourselves and others to close it
- use the systems mapping processes to reinforce awareness and motivation and to start to define methods for closing the gap.

We soon found that Van Gundy's list would be of little use to us. There is nothing actually wrong with his model for simple, discrete, contained problems. But its profound over-simplification obscures the real challenges to effecting any change when dealing with complex systemic problems. The inadequacies of the model are twofold:

- It does not explore the nature of problems but confines them to a simple and, in principle, measurable gap.

- It skates over the issues of individual and personal perspective which define 'what should be' and therefore the nature of the gap. Further, it obscures the issues of self-interest which affect motivation.

Complex problems: messes

Clearly, problems vary in their complexity, and that complexity has different dimensions. Some highly technical complex problems can be addressed by techniques such as operational research. Other complex problems cannot. Ackoff[17] makes a useful distinction between 'problems' and 'messes'. He says:

> Managers are not confronted with problems which are independent of each other, but with dynamic situations that consist of complex systems of changing problems that interact with each other. I call such situations messes. Problems are abstractions extracted from messes by analysis; they are to messes as atoms are to tables and chairs.

The emphasis needs to be on the management of messes rather than the solving of problems. If 'mess' describes the systems with which we are dealing, it is clear that these messes will not be improved by the optimisation of solutions to independent problems.

We realised that the notion of 'mess' applies in a clinical as well as an organisational context. We referred earlier to the nature of chronic ill health and the tendency for older people to suffer from multiple conditions. The present writer's own mother is seventy five and suffers from a heart condition, Parkinson's disease and osteoporosis. She wouldn't thank him for saying so but she is a 'mess' in the Ackoff sense and, while being treated by specialists (cardiology, neurology and orthopaedics) with a single-problem focus, she is also managed by a geriatrician who is the only professional who recognises the emergent complexity of her physical and psychological health.

The problem of trying to solve the problem – illustrations from our early work.

Solutions that move the problem elsewhere

In our early diagnostic work we asked people to think up their favourite solution before we mapped the system. When they saw the larger system they universally rejected their first thoughts. They recognised that their 'solutions' may seem better from where they stand but just moved the problem somewhere else in the system – they recognised the inevitability of unintended consequences in complex, interconnected, systems. They realised that sticking with their original solution might just optimise the status quo – it didn't provide any new options.

How you describe the problem defines whose problem it is and foreshadows action

Take, for example, older people's fear about going out on the streets. If 'the problem' is described as 'youngsters intimidating elders', then you may keep possible allies fragmented. If 'the problem' is discussed with young men present, they too talk of feeling bullied by groups of people of their own age hanging about on the street corners. Now there is a new and shared issue which is inter-generational. This can be recast as 'how do we get to feel safer on the street?', and then we have even more potential allies and collaborators.

Changing the way in which this kind of problem was described led to some spectacular results in New York, where a counter-intuitive intervention was linked to a dramatic fall in the murder rate. In the traditional problem-solving mode they would have put extra policemen on murder inquiries – 'targeted resources on the greatest need'. Instead, new police activity was focused on making the streets feel safer by reducing the threatening behaviours and activities of, for example, graffiti artists, squeegee merchants and aggressive beggars.

There may be some parallel in the way the words 'hospital discharge' prescribe the parameters of the issue and limit people's attitudes. Though inpatient discharge procedures have probably improved, the public perception is still that people are discharged unaided in the middle of the night. On probing, these stories relate to 'discharge' from casualty departments. The public do not distinguish between the departments involved. It is possible that there would be a greater increase in public confidence if any extra effort was spent on training taxi drivers to take people home (including climbing the stairs and putting on the lights), rather than more and more effort into discharge planning for a minority of patients at the 'serious' end of this experience, where most effort is currently concentrated.

A spectrum of complexity: from 'tame' to 'wicked' problems

Rittel & Weber[18] have written about the varying complexity of problems and also pick up the issues of different stakeholder perspectives and motivations. They distinguish between 'tame' and 'wicked' problems.

A *tame problem* is one which can be specified in a form agreed by any relevant parties ahead of the analysis and which does not change during the analysis.

A *'wicked' problem*, by contrast, is dynamic and ill defined; there are many alternative types and levels of explanation for the phenomena of concern, and any selected type of explanation determines the nature of the solution. Alternative solutions are not true or false but good or bad, and there are interested parties with conflicting perspectives whose value judgements are all important.

'Messes' and 'wickedness' are evident in the complex systems of health and social care in which the LHP is working.

Complex problems and the dimension of conflict

The mess is likely to be augmented if the differing perspectives of system stakeholders create opportunities for conflict between them. Pava[19] has addressed the interrelationship between conflict and task complexity in organisations.

He uses a two-by-two matrix to distinguish between four categories of situation: high and low complexity, and high and low conflict. He recommends different change strategies for each of the combinations. A classical planning approach, which allows exhaustive analysis, formulation of the problem and detailed planning of the solution, is only possible in situations of relatively low complexity and low conflict. When the task is complex but the conflict remains low then participative approaches to redesign are possible in which stakeholders can engage in reformulation of the problem and the joint creation of solutions.

'Technical rationality', however, as defined by Stacey[12], inhibits action in situations of high conflict. Technical rationality demands that the problem will be formulated and clearly articulated, and that specific solution options will be generated and explored. In fact, this approach provides an arena for conflict. Situations can easily degenerate into data wars in which opposing sides deploy ever more sophisticated 'evidence' to support their contrasting positions. In such situations of conflict and complexity, Stacey has pointed out, managers will try to reduce the risk to themselves and their organisations by:

- refraining from action altogether
- looking for less risky actions
- breaking the action down into smaller steps
- trying to forecast the outcome and then later arguing that none could have foreseen what happened
- trying to reduce their stake in the action by diluting personal responsibility in a group decision or by involving other groups and organisations in the action.

Implications for LHP practice

Our exploration provides a health warning about the application of linear, simple, diagnostic paradigms and problem solving techniques to complex systems and situations with high conflict potential. We were left puzzling about:

- Why identify 'problems' when solving them won't help the 'mess'?
- With 'wicked' problems, to define the problem is to foreshadow the solution, so how can they be tackled?
- Why articulate solutions when to do so will only mobilise resistance?

Chapter 4

The Urban Dimension

As we explained in Chapter one, inner city primary care is one of the well-recognised 'problems' of delivering health care. Though there have been substantial improvements in service provision in cities in recent years the gap between cities and towns and county areas may even have widened. London GPs seem more dissatisfied than other groups of GPs, and recent investments through fundholding and the LIZ initiative have, largely, failed to impact on their disgruntlement. How are we to understand this?

Most of us seek to explain this dilemma in relation to some deficiency in one or other of the parts of the system – there is something wrong with London or city GPs, with the city population, with the quality of management, etc. We began to think about it in another way. Perhaps it was not that the parts were in some way wrong but that the way health services work in cities is different. If we apply a systems approach, for example, then the city itself can be seen as a complex system which cannot be understood by simply trying to understand the individual parts. We have started to look at how cities work and find both challenge and explanation in the work of the American philosopher Jane Jacobs[20].

We were also aware that the strategic issues facing London's health services in the early 1990s would soon apply to our other major cities – how to design the hospitals of the future at the same time as extending the capacity of community-based health services.

The contribution of the Urban Primary Care Network

We decided to form an **Urban Primary Care Network** consisting of managers and clinicians responsible for the delivery and development of primary care in a number of British cities. Several major cities are represented and participants come from general practice, health commissions, universities, community health services, community health councils, and the NHS executive. We believed that there would be a set of issues that related particularly to the delivery of primary care in cities, and that people in different parts of the country could learn from each other.

This group has been very useful to us in helping develop ideas and we set out below some of the key issues they have helped us to clarify.

Innovation

Our colleagues in the Urban Primary Care Network were rather tired of endless claims to innovative practice made by NHS organisations and individuals, and weary of exhortations from within the NHS hierarchy to 'be more innovative'. As we found during the large scale consultations, it was often the simple things which were done badly. It seemed to us that what was needed was some action, not more hot ideas.

Walker and Henry sum this up in the Introduction to *Managing Innovation*[21]

Having ideas is relatively easy – having good ideas is slightly more difficult - but the real challenge lies in carrying ideas through into some practical result ... most acts of creativity are doomed to failure. Ideas themselves are fragile, the processes to which they are subject are uncertain and often hostile, the organisational filters are severely applied and the world at large might show a quite astonishing indifference to the brilliant brainchild.

We now think that our collective irritation with the mantra of innovation stemmed from our confusion of the concepts of *innovation* and *invention*. Innovation is a process stretching from the first tentative recognition of need or possibility, through invention to implementation and diffusion. We realised that we were in fact happy with innovation if this meant new practical things in the real world but not if it was confined to the need and invention end of the continuum. We were much more interested in the implementation of old ideas than the invention of new ones.

Projects and 'projectitis'

The Urban Primary Care Network warned us about the dangers of 'soft', time-limited, money and the project bidding process by which agencies generally acquired this money. They felt that such processes were more of a managerial distraction than a help and that the resultant projects were rarely successful in making real change to the ways in which mainstream work was effected. They described the influence of widespread project working on their organisations as 'projectitis'.[22]

In the light of our earlier discussion of complex systems, problems and solutions, it came as no surprise that the impact of most projects on complex systems of care is minimal. Projects epitomise rational planning processes: problem definition and the setting of objectives are followed by a series of developments which it is expected will bring about the required end point. The circumstances in which projects work are therefore somewhat limited.

Innovative projects, pilots and roll-outs

Our colleagues described how many health and social care agencies conduct development through a sequence of pilot project, project evaluation and roll-out (to transfer the development project from the setting in which it appeared to work to new settings). We identified at least three difficulties that arise from the attempt to roll-out.

- If the pilot has been conducted in a complex system, how can the evaluator be sure that observable changes in that system are causally related to the activities of the project?
- It is unlikely that the problem, to which the original project was a potential solution, will be duplicated in other complex systems, though there may be superficial similarities.
- The systems context in which the pilot is conducted is very unlikely to be reproduced elsewhere.

These reservations mean that the relevance of pilot projects to other settings is likely to be very limited and the generalisability of 'solutions' even more limited. This is not to say that useful and generalisable learning about process cannot take place, but the successful duplication of pilots will be rare.

City dimensions

Through our joint enquiry and our reading we came to two useful and clear insights about the way in which primary health care in cities was distinct from primary health care in other contexts. The first was a recognition of its diversity, and a realisation that this diversity could be a potential source of richness rather than a problem. The second was to do with perceptions and attitudes. We realised that it would be more productive if we stopped thinking about primary health care in cities as in some way *deviant*, but recognised that, in fact, it was just *different*.

Innovation 'champions' and the generalisability of solutions

At the same time as we were discussing and reading about cities we were looking at material on how new ideas or inventions get transferred and taken-up. Where technological invention is concerned, Shon[23] has described 'product champions' as critical in the transition from invention to innovation. In his early work he analysed a range of radical military innovations and concluded that:

- at the outset a new idea encounters sharp resistance
- overcoming this resistance requires vigorous promotion
- proponents of the idea have to work primarily through the informal rather than the formal organisation
- typically one person (or one group) emerges as the champion of the idea

This discussion led us to hypothesise that the generalisability of a solution is proportional to

- the degree to which both the original problem and its solution can be specified
- the degree to which the contexts of the original and the 'duplicate' problem can be specified
- the degree to which these contexts match
- the degree to which the solution is effectively championed.

We posit that in complex systems the concepts of problems and solutions are not too useful. Complex systems are dynamic so the comparability of context over time, let alone across systems, is very limited. Product champions may arise but the 'wickedness' of problems in complex systems means that multiple stakeholders will always have different perspectives. Furthermore, championship may actually undermine the possibility of innovation by stimulating resistance and defensive behaviours.

On a continuum of generalisable 'designed' solutions, accounting software packages, for example, would be highly generalisable, surgical techniques somewhere in the middle and care packages for unwell older people at the low end.

Summary so far

The following short statements sum up where we'd got to at this stage:

Aspiration

to develop a distinctive programme of work to address intractable, elephant, boundary problems of relevance to the well being of older people

Who with

with older people themselves and with the complex systems of care and welfare that support them

Why

because of the findings from the diagnostic processes, and their implications for action

Nature of the issues

emergent 'messes' and 'wicked' problems; situations of high complexity and conflict leading to difficulty in making appropriate interventions

What to avoid

project interventions and time limited 'soft money', which rarely lead to sustainable change.

Chapter 5

Finding new methods and theories

Discovering ways of working with large groups

We now come to one of those tricky points where to determine the sequence of action and theory is almost impossible. We were seeking new ways to achieve our key objectives which were:

- to enhance the system of health and social care for older people
- to distribute largesse without stipulating a project/bidding model
- to generate insights about how systems worked, as the diagnostic events had done, but to include more participants and spread the ideas further
- to empower and involve service users throughout the process.

We began to discover a cluster of methods for working with large groups which were being developed principally in the USA. They had been used mainly for consultancy so had not been evaluated. Evidence of their effectiveness and impact was limited, but they embodied certain characteristics which suggested they might help us achieve our objectives. We referred to them as 'whole systems events':

- they tended to be discrete, time-bounded, events
- they could include large numbers of people – in Weisbord's[31] phrase, they could 'get the whole system in the room'
- they took a systems view
- they embraced the idea of complexity and did not attempt to tidy up and simplify things
- they used participative and democratic methods
- they seemed to hold out the possibility of triggering significant change for individuals and organisations, and in the relationships between them
- they aimed to generate new, radical options, not to optimise current circumstances.

The nature of the theory behind whole systems events

We started to explore the practice and theory behind these whole systems interventions. We knew we could get advice and support to help us learn how to use the methods but we felt it was also essential that we had some grasp of the underlying theory. We knew from experience that using structured methods, uninformed by theory, could lead to the methods becoming fetishised. Practitioners could become obsessed with ritual adherence to the method for its own sake, irrespective of any relationship between their actions and the outcomes they were trying to achieve. The following quotations reflected some of our reasoning at the time.

Theory is the body of statement, taken as a related whole, that is used as the basis for design, judgement and guidance of action ...when a company (or any other kind of organisation) evolves without sufficient thinking and awareness at the level of theory, then the fixes and adaptations to circumstances create an increasingly complicated system in which the rule book is the only salvation.[24]

There is nothing so practical as a good theory.[25]

We also knew that if we used these new whole systems methods we were asking participants to take a risk – committing themselves to a process the outcomes of which were unknowable. We were aware that most sensible people would fight shy of following us if we seemed to be blatantly making it up as went along. So, in order to persuade others to join us, as well as to understand and critically evaluate the methods, we needed to understand the theory.

According to Casti[26], scientific theories or rules have four key attributes. They are:

- *explicit* – there is no ambiguity in the statement of the rule and it requires no private interpretation to employ the rule for prediction or explanation
- *reliable* – they have stood the test of time
- *objective* – they are relatively free of investigator bias
- *public* – they are open to public scrutiny.

However, it soon became clear to us that there was no agreed scientific theory underpinning the whole systems methods. In common with much of human social evolution, practice had preceded theory. The only criteria met by WSEs was the last one – they are public events.

We realised that these new, large-group, whole systems methods had arisen from their inventors' subjective beliefs about how change occurs. And we learnt that there was much debate about what did and did not work, and about why the methods achieved what they appeared to[30]. We were reminded of our own early discussions about the difficulty of causal attribution in complex systems as we realised that, at this stage in the development of WSEs, the relationship between method, performance and outcome was unclear. We also acknowledged that the nature of these relationships might remain ambiguous.

New theories of change in complex adaptive systems

Our growing understanding of systems perspectives had given us a few concepts that we could apply to organisations and social systems to help us understand how they worked. These included:

- the importance of focusing on relationships and connections between parts, people and organisations
- the realisation that you cannot get a sense of how a whole system works by trying to understanding how the separate parts work
- the notion that all systems can be understood at a number of levels, and that each level has its own emergent properties
- the idea that networks are the common pattern of organisation in systems, that they are non-linear and sustained through feedback loops.

Autopoiesis, self-organisation, self-reference or identity

During this time we were also discovering new theories about change in complex adaptive systems. Complex adaptive systems, we learnt, are systems in which what emerges is not only greater than the sum of the parts but it also changes as a result of experience (for example the human brain, or the human body). Such systems we discovered, can be highly stable and ordered at the same time as being capable of adaptive change. This presented us with a seeming paradox – that something can both change and remain the same. We found ourselves struggling to understand organisations as complex adaptive systems (and what to do as a consequence!).

To start to unravel this mystery we looked at the work of several writers in the fields of physics, biology and cognition. We found that writers such as Prigogine, Lovelock, and Maturana[27, 28, 29] provided us with useful components to help us elucidate the theory. These included:

- the idea of *autopoiesis* – the ability of a complex adaptive system to renew itself (i.e., to stay the same, to maintain its identity)

- the concept of *self-organisation* – the ability of a complex adaptive system to utilise energy to generate new behaviour patterns or structures from simple underlying rules (i.e., to change)

- the idea of *self-reference* or *identity* – the observation that a complex adaptive system can only change in ways that are consistent with its existing identity, not at random (i.e. adaptation or evolution).

These concepts helped us to begin to make sense of the idea that complex adaptive systems could both retain their identity and adapt/co-evolve along with their environment.

We also identified the characteristics of those complex adaptive systems in which emergence can take place. They need to have:

- networks of interconnected parts
- critical patterns of connections
- sufficient closed feedback loops
- [be] on the edge of equilibrium
- behaviour guided by simple rules or guiding principles that can change

The word 'autopoiesis' (literally 'self-making') was coined by Maturana and Varela, two Chilean neuroscientists working on a biological theory of cognition. Maturana hypothesised that

> *living systems ... are organised in a closed, causal, circular process that allows for evolutionary change in the way circularity is maintained, but not for the loss of the circularity itself.*[29]

Since all changes in the system take place within this basic circularity, Maturana argued that the components that specify the organisation must also be produced and maintained by it. He concluded that this network pattern, in which the function of each component is to help produce and transform other components, while maintaining the overall circularity of the network (i.e. its identity), is the basic 'organisation of the living'.

He deduced that self-organising systems are also continually self-referring, so that, for example, perception cannot be viewed as the representation of an external reality, but must be understood as the continual creation of new relationships within the neural network (i.e. there is no existing, absolute external world – only what the perceiver brings forth. For example, we 'see' the world as coloured and some insects 'see' it as temperature graded). He postulated that 'living systems are cognitive systems, and living is a process of cognition'.

Maturana and Varela also make an important distinction between 'organisation' and 'structure'.

> *Organisation … denotes those relations that must exist among the components of a system for it to be a member of a specific class. Structure denotes the components and relations that actually constitute a particular unity, and make its organisation real.*[29]

A system's structure is thus the physical embodiment of its organisation. They stress the system's organisation is independent of the properties of its components, so that a given organisation can take different forms, and be made up of many different kinds of components. For example, for something to be a bicycle there must exist certain relationships between its constituent parts of wheels, frame, pedals and so on. But the components and relationships can vary to produce a whole range of bicycles from the penny farthing to the mountain bike – different structures, same organisation.

In *human* systems, we have the additional process of consciousness (self-awareness). While all living systems are aware of the environment, social beings are conscious of that awareness. In the theory of Maturana and Varela, consciousness is closely allied to language. Language embodies communication about communication. And communication is not about the transmission of information, but about the co-ordination of behaviour.

Applying these theories to practice

We were fortunate to develop a relationship with two US consultants, Margaret Wheatley and Myron Kellner-Rogers, who helped us take these ideas into the organisations we were working with. Between them they have probably done more than anyone else to develop these ideas and to search for ways of applying them in practice. They identify three factors as central to the change process in complex human systems. These are information, relationships and what they call 'self-reference', or 'identity'. The following quotes from Margaret Wheatley's book Leadership and the New Sciences[15], give some flavour of their approach.

> *There is something here that is fundamentally important, and that is the distinction that order is different from control. When you seek to control things, you must manage all of the pieces; you must know what is going on everywhere in the organisation; you must have job descriptions; you must really have your hands on all of the pieces because, in fact, your function as leader is to hold it all together. One of the things I am very clear on is that order is inherent in living systems. It is part of what makes things work, with or without us. Even in an organisation, I believe there is an order that can emerge. And the order is not from telling people what to do, defining it, and writing procedures. The order is inherent, and we need to allow people enormous freedom with the understanding that the principles and the values will order their behaviour.*

The system is autopoietic, focusing its activities on what is required to maintain its own integrity and self-renewal. As it changes, it does so by referring to itself: whatever future form it takes will be consistent with its already established identity. Changes do not occur randomly, in any direction. They always are consistent with what has gone on before, with the history and identity of the system...

If we allow autonomy at the local level, letting individuals or units be directed in their decisions by guideposts for organisational self-reference, we can achieve coherence and continuity. Self-organisation succeeds when the system supports the independent activity of its members by giving them, quite literally, a strong frame of reference. When it does this, the global system achieves even greater levels of autonomy and integrity.

They use a checklist that helps them to develop a systems focus when they start to work with a new, mixed group of people in a locality:

- what is the relevant system?
- does it know that it is a system?
- does it have access to itself in terms of the information, relationships, and self-reference/identity that maintain and renew it?
- what does the system want to happen?

We have used these (and other) ideas to help guide our work, but have a long way to go before we can be confident we are applying them in an appropriate and coherent way. We believe that groups of local people can come up with their own solutions without the need for imported 'experts' – in other words, they have the capacity to become self-organising systems. Our question is how do we support self-organising activity? We know that we cannot direct systems, but can only perturb them. By this we mean

- change the way a system sees itself
- change the way it sees its relationship with its environment
- set up and complete feedback loops
- make new connections to allow different communication

We are looking for processes that shift the focus from solving problems to creating a shared view of what is significant.

Much of our subsequent work has been to seek ways of explaining these abstract ideas through stories based on the circumstances of our local partners and our experience of working with them.

Chapter 6

Selecting a whole system method

The operational group continued to investigate WSEs in a number of ways. We made contact with two management consultants from the USA, Billie Alban and Barbara Bunker, who in 1992 had co-edited a special edition of the Journal of Applied Behavioural Science on Large Group Interventions[30]. We found their journal highly informative and stimulating. We arranged for them to run a seminar on large group interventions for representatives from health and social care systems who were interested in working with us.

As a result of these investigations and discussions, we were eventually drawn to two very different kinds of WSE. These were 'Future Search Conferences', developed and documented by Marvin Weisbord[31], and 'Open Space Technology', developed by Harrison Owen[32]. We were interested in these approaches for a number of reasons, but in particular they seemed appropriate to our circumstances, and best able to quell our anxiety and that of our collaborators.

Anxiety management

We thought Open Space and Future Search would help us manage our anxiety for the following reasons.

- We were in touch with consultants in the USA and Europe who were experienced in using these methods and could advise us.

- Both methods were well tried and seemed culturally robust. They had been used in several kinds of organisational and community settings in many different parts of the world.

- We thought these two kinds of events stood a good chance of working in the UK: we could see how people could become purposefully engaged in them, and we felt we could run them without embarrassing ourselves.

Appropriate for our circumstances

We also considered that these two methods were well-suited to our purposes and circumstances.

- Both approaches allowed the group to create the agenda for change.

- Both included plenty of small group work, and gave opportunities for participants to work in several different groups with a whole range of people in the system.

- Both methods required the wide sharing of information generated by the whole group.

- Neither method assumed a pre-existing shared culture or history. In Future Search the sharing of perceptions of history was part of the process; Open Space just required that the participating group was interested in the theme to be addressed.

• Neither method was concerned with analysing and solving existing problems by rejigging or optimising the present state of affairs.

Furthermore, we thought both these methods had the potential to generate the kind of information and understandings that would enable participants to see themselves as a system. We expected new relationships to develop across the system. We expected that the events would give participants a better insight into questions such as: 'How did our system get to be the way it is?'; 'What do we value?'; 'Why are we, as a system, acting in this way?'. These questions lie at the heart of the concept of self-reference or identity.

Identifying the system

We had established from the early diagnostic events with older people that the services and agencies which affected their well-being extended way beyond the statutory health and social services. We knew that a whole host of apparently unconnected services, facilities and social interactions, could have a profound impact on the quality of older people's lives, ranging from such things as local policing policy, and the accessibility of shopping facilities and the availability of transport, to the attentiveness of the postman and the milkman. We were therefore determined that the events would incorporate as many of these diverse elements of 'the system' as possible. The actual invitees were to be identified by planning groups set up to organise the events (see next chapter), but we took advice from our US colleague, Myron Kellner-Rogers, to 'go beyond all the usual suspects' and set the system boundaries loosely in terms of both players and geography. If new relationships and ways of working were to emerge from the process, we needed fertile ground in which to work.

Chapter 7

Planning and running the first whole systems events

We began to plan our first WSEs confident that we would find partners who appreciated that

- the system of health care for older people involves many agencies, organisations and individuals
- intractable problems need a systems approach
- the old ways of tackling these problems do not work.

We were less confident that we could carry out two whole system interventions within the tight timetable proposed by the LHP Steering Group. To try to meet the deadline we worked with two sites which had taken part in the earlier systems mapping exercise.

We worked through the core elements of the process with support from our more experienced colleagues in long transatlantic telephone calls. And we slavishly followed their instructions. For example, we were told group tables should be round and 5ft in diameter – no more and no less; and that conference rooms should have natural daylight – which wasn't easy to find, and continues to cause us problems finding appropriate venues. Only later were we really convinced that these details were more than mere ritual. We tried 6ft tables, and they were simply too big for people to hold a group conversation.

Whatever kind of large system event was being planned, the first step was always to engage the local CEOs, or their equivalents, and then negotiate their support and involvement. Next we would set up a planning group with a broad range of interested people who were not 'all the usual suspects'. This group needed to have the wherewithal and authority to carry out the following tasks:

- to identify the issue or question for the whole systems event – which should not be so narrow that every participant would arrive with their pet solution, nor so broad that participants would not understand why they had been invited
- to construct an invitation list
- to provide logistical support for the preparation and build-up to the event and during the event
- to make preliminary provision to support any follow-up activity undertaken by self-organising groups formed at the event.

We assumed that the large events would have significant numbers of older people as participants, and that the events would generate a process which would continue afterwards. We knew little about how this follow-on activity could be supported and though we were beginning to comprehend the general principles underpinning the interventions, our understanding of the detail was sketchy.

We worked on the first two WSEs concurrently in order to complete them by the end of the summer 1995. This put pressure on the planning process and clouded ownership (was it an LHP or a local event?). We also soon realised that the planning process was undermined by adopting standard 'committee behaviour', such as meeting for one to two hour slots with a chair and formal agendas, and meticulous minute taking.

In the Autumn we started work in three more sites. We moved to fewer but longer planning meetings, which enabled us to mix inputs about the theoretical underpinning with practical planning. Now we began to experience the start up process as repetitive. We were trying to draw in and connect a disparate range of local people, and that often meant working with different individuals from one meeting to the next. Sometimes regular attendees seemed unable to retain, or link, what had happened from one meeting to the next. We frequently found ourselves having to go back to the beginning or saying the same things over and over again. It took us a while to realise that what we were experiencing was in fact the 'necessary redundancy' and 'reiteration' described in the theory of complex systems – it was essential to repeat things many times because people picked things up bit by bit and only gradually made connections between ideas and each other. We began to acknowledge that the process of planning was itself a critical part of the intervention.

What happens at the whole system events and immediately afterwards

These large group interventions are highly structured processes yet they generate long-term unpredictable outcomes. Impacts differ in each place, and according to the type of event[30]. However, from experience we have come to 'predict' some immediate effects:

- a lot of energy and enthusiasm is generated
- the experience is enjoyable and builds or rebuilds solidarity
- new working relationships are made through putting faces to names
- the conference report which lists all participants makes a new, extensive contact list
- many elderly participants want to be involved in follow-up activities
- participants develop new skills in running meetings that encourage involvement and value equally different contributions
- 'common ground' themes formulated during the events may reinforce old priorities but also give legitimacy for new areas of work
- 'necessary conditions' identified during the events indicate how the common ground issues might be addressed – crucial contributions if we are to do things differently
- action plans may be developed at the events by individuals or groups
- several action or 'possibility' groups form, with a named convenor so people can get in touch.

Many of these 'immediate products' of the events are about new or improved relationships and better connections within the system. At this stage, we believe that to sustain the work we have to continue to engage with three groups: chief executives, the planning groups, and the action or possibility groups.

How we should engage with local agencies became clearer with more experience. Over time we have been able to describe our expectations, suggest a phased engagement process and set out the nature of the 'contract' we would like to have with agencies.

Each stage in the process requires the LHP team to adopt methods congruent with systems-thinking and invite participants to do the same. We run meetings in different ways, with unusual mixes of people and explicitly involve new people in ways which transcend the usual consultation processes.

We think there are certain ways of working which characterise whole systems interventions – from the small planning meetings to the large group events:

- unusual mixes of people are brought together (to support new and generative relationships)
- these unusual combinations of people spend sufficient time together to move beyond first impressions
- they work together in the same room at the same time to produce 'real time work'. This is in contrast to more usual ways of producing ideas and action plans for change which start with consultation, followed in sequence by report-writing, circulation, comment, rewrite and so on.
- the pitfalls of problem solving approaches are avoided by searching for possibilities not solutions. The term 'conversations for possibility', a term coined by McMaster, best describes this process.

Chapter 8

What happens after whole systems events

Our expectations

This is where the trail goes cold in the literature. Most of what we read, and the advice we received from consultants, was about the planning of WSEs and the conduct and dynamics of the events themselves. We found only a few references to WSE methods being used as regular ways of working within organisations, and little else about these methods as part of a continuing process.

The only explicit advice we received on follow-up was that planning groups should try to set up, in advance, the resources and processes which would facilitate the actions proposed during the event. When we shared this recommendation with the planning groups we were faced with blank incredulity. How was it possible to set up support for actions that were as yet unknown and entirely unpredictable? We were, sadly, unable to elaborate.

Yet, proponents of these methods seemed to expect that the events would be transformational. They believed that the energy, insights, information and new relationships generated by the events would be enough to sustain on-going activities which would bring about the desired changes. We never really believed this. Our scepticism was based not on logic, but on a belief that such a powerful, one-off, intervention was just too good to be true. We had vigorously eschewed other kinds of magic bullets and we were not going to start believing in this one. We had recognised quite early on that the events would be part of a process which would need to continue long after the event itself was over. We expected that these processes would be largely self-organising but we did not expect them to be entirely self-sustaining. We believed this because our experience as change agents in other settings led us to this conclusion.

We hoped and expected that the events would be enjoyable and energising. That the new relationships created would be generative and would lead to new collaborative ways of working, and that the shared information and insights would lead to participants reframing issues and widening and sharing their 'mental maps'. What we did not expect was that these developments, arising from the event alone, would be enough to radically enhance the system and improve the well-being of older people .

We were also aware that we had become mesmerised by the design of future search events which culminated in 'action planning' and, despite our best intentions, were in danger of falling back into 'project mode'. We realised that action planning groups formed at future search events might turn out to be just another way of splitting problems into bits, or of taking easier options with more knowable outcomes, or of avoiding dealing with the complexity of situations altogether. (We reminded ourselves of our earlier reading of Stacey[12], see page 38.)

However, we now realise that the WSEs do, in fact, generate energy that is self-sustaining. New information, new relationships and new communication channels – that is, new *connections* – brought about by the WSE continue to generate energy long after the event itself.

However, we also know that momentum is more easily sustained with extra energy from an external source, such as the continued inputs of the LHP operational group. These insights are in fact consistent with theories of complex adaptive systems, in particular with the ideas of self-organisation, and of dissipative structures as exemplified by Stacey in Strategic Management & Organisational Dynamics[12].

Outcomes from whole system events

There are two outcomes from WSEs which we believe could be more effectively exploited. These are the shared ideas and records ('artefacts') created during the event and the new organisations ('action groups') formed as a result of the event.

Artefacts

The events create a set of ideas and a language which facilitate subsequent communication between participants, and which can be used to educate, influence and involve the wider community. Indeed, successful follow-up and change can only be achieved if the ideas and concrete initiatives identified by groups at the event are understood and supported by the community at large.

- Videos and written accounts of the actual events give a powerful impression of their scale and diversity, and the active and creative processes in which participants engage.

- Participants produce 'visions of a future service' and the entire assemblage draws out 'the common ground'. The common ground themes are immediately comprehensible and relevant to the community, and powerfully legitimated by the wide range and authority of the participants.

- Participants at Future Search events, in particular, identify 'necessary conditions' which are required to actualise the 'visions of the future'. These necessary conditions constitute, in themselves, a potential agenda for change.

Action groups

Groups of individuals with shared interests develop during WSEs, and many of them continue afterwards as action groups. They may try to achieve a particular task, or to spread new ideas, by influencing and drawing in others who are affected by the issue and have a part to play. We are beginning to learn about the kind of support action groups need to help them work in new ways – to maintain the equal participation of older people, to work with multiple perspectives and to resist deferring to traditional power structures and solutions.

We now believe that these groups are new, embryonic, organisations which could be considered as dissipative structures[12]. We prefer to refer to them as 'possibility groups' rather than 'action groups'. If we think of these groupings as new kinds of organisations we can then start to think about how to help support and sustain them.

The emergence of new ways of working

We are pleasantly surprised by the emergence of new ways of working which were neither planned nor have arisen directly from the action groups. A network of new and unusual relationships seems to grow, drawing in and connecting even people who were not at the original event.

A metaphor derived from the flooding of the Nile has proved helpful when thinking about how to support new ways of working across systems. The annual inundation brings forth many possibilities and is necessary to the renewal and fertility of the alluvial plain. However, much of the potential resource will simply drain away – as will much of the enthusiasm surrounding the whole systems events. The task facing local people is to harness as much of the power as possible. In the case of the Nile, one solution, favoured until quite recently, was to control that power by building a huge dam. However, the resulting social and ecological damage soon become clear. The harmful impact of the dam is an example of an unintended dysfunctional consequence arising from a single intervention in a complex system. The puzzle is therefore how to create conditions for the resource to be harnessed which work with the process of inundation rather than against it – how to make appropriate interventions in complex systems. This will be the focus of the operational group's work in the coming year.

We continue to travel hopefully because:

- So many things, both large and small, happen during the follow-up period after whole systems events. Some recent examples include:

  a housing association using methods from whole systems meetings to improve participation in their meetings

  modifying existing work by involving elders: for example, a physiotherapy department and a leisure centre inviting elders to help them devise ageism awareness training

  speeding up of things that are already in the pipeline: for example, a one-stop information shop

  altering an EU-funded information technology programme to focus on the housing needs of older people

  a new initiative on developing strategy for hospital discharge in a city.

- The ideas and methods we are developing seem plausible to ever more people struggling with intractable problems. All kinds of people seem willing to take a risk and engage with us in a 'joint enquiry' without guarantee of predictable outcomes.

- We, and our local partners, are more certain we are on the right lines since we discovered similar partnerships across systems in other cities.

- The methods we are using do enable people, particularly older people, to feel confident that they can participate in 'making a difference'.

Appendix I

Progress report at 6 months

Londoners and the health service changes

Like most capital cities, London has extremes of wealth and poverty, immense racial and cultural diversity, growing numbers of elderly people without family support, people who are inadequately housed or homeless, as well as many thousands of people who travel daily to work or to seek work there. These factors have always posed challenges for the NHS and never more so than now, when our health care system is being reshaped by powerful social, demographic and economic pressures.

Throughout the industrialised world, health systems are having to respond to changing patterns of need for many conditions, the long-term management of chronic ill health has become as relevant as the treatment of its acute episodes. Technological changes mean that much of the care that is traditionally given in outpatient departments, or hospital beds, or accident departments can potentially be delivered much closer to people's homes. These changes are also being brought about by numerous user groups who have demanded and won changes to health care delivery. Increasingly, there is a preference from users for community-based services. The hospital of the future is likely to be smaller and more specialised.

Primary care, that is health care outside hospitals, is seen as one of the key building blocks of the future. In our system, general practice is the cornerstone of primary care.

Definitions of primary care are notoriously difficult but this attempts to capture its essence:

> *Primary care is a network of community-based health services that covers prevention of ill health, treatment of acute and chronic illness, rehabilitation, support at home for patients who are frail elderly, disabled or acutely or chronically ill, and terminal care.*

> *As a whole primary care is much less visible and less well understood than hospital care. Yet, these are the services that make it possible in this country to manage 90 per cent of care outside hospitals, to limit patients' length of stay in hospital and discharge them safely, and to maintain at home people who do not want to be institutionalised.*

Those who live and work in London know that its primary care services are underdeveloped. Paradoxically, the great hospital institutions of London have both provided a safety net and made it difficult for primary care to flourish. Things may well get worse before they get better. The fear is that the most vulnerable Londoners will suffer most. The transition from our current institution-led service to one which better meets the needs of Londoners will not be easy. The build-up of primary care services may not be fast enough but the momentum for change is inescapable. And now is the time to influence the shape of health care for Londoners for the next 25 years.

The Government has already begun a major investment programme aimed principally at getting the basics right, such as improving premises for general practice and retraining staff. The London Health Partnership wants to use its resources effectively to add value to what is already beginning to happen.

Consultation

When the Partnership was being formed, we consulted widely among charitable trusts, community groups, GPs, and networks of London health professionals and managers. Three clear messages emerged.

Not innovations. What was wanted was not innovations or inventions but help with the intractable problems of urban primary care, such as services for mentally ill people or vulnerable elderly people whose experience is often of chronic conditions as well as acute episodes of illness, and who depend on more than one agency for support. **The Partnership has decided that the focus of its work will be better ways of providing services for elderly people in or near their own homes.**

Not projects. While the need for investment is great, it is extremely difficult to bring about lasting change with short-term project money which has to be bid for on a hurried, competitive basis. 'Projectitis' becomes a distraction rather than a help. **The Partnership has decided not to seek project proposals at this stage but to help with new ways of thinking about using development monies.**

Not more of the same. **The Partnership should be about trying to do things differently at a time of unprecedented change.**

London-wide meetings

We decided that the first phase of work (June-November 1994) would consist of London-wide meetings with elderly Londoners themselves and local workshops in London districts to understand more about the barriers to change.

In July 1994, we contacted as many London-wide agencies as we could (e.g. Age Concern, Greater London Association of Community Health Councils, Pensioners Forum). We wrote to their local branches, asking each of them to pass on our invitation to six elderly people known to them. We targeted ethnic minority groups, and we used our health service contacts to reach district nurses, home help organisers and general practices. We sent out 3500 invitations in all. Over 200 people, from all over the city, attended the workshops in September and October.

The purpose of the meetings was to hear the personal experiences of the elderly people taking part and turn these into opportunities for improving services. A video crew and graphic artist helped to capture some of the richness of the events (see page 9). The themes, which emerged, include the following.

Variations

Surprise at the extent of variation in different parts of London - not only in the services which are free in some places and not in others, but also the variation in the services themselves (e.g. home helps who do X in one place and Y in another).

Ageism

Concerns that professionals do not listen to elderly people; that some treatments seem to be valued more than others (e.g. cancer care rather than dementia which is seen as an illness of old age); that there is age-related rationing (e.g. mammography, mobility allowance).

Anger/fear

Sense of anger, fear and confusion about the rules changing fast and the goalposts being moved ('We fought for the NHS and now it's disappearing. Some bits have fallen off already, e.g. eyes and teeth. What next?'). "Battling' and 'fighting' were the words used about trying to be heard or to get information about services and entitlements.

Anxiety

Partly the uncertainty of growing old, compounded with the sense that no one explains things well or takes the views of old people seriously. Being connected to a voluntary organisation which acts as an advocate was much valued.

Services in people's own homes

Concerns about how to monitor the quality of people who come into one's own home to deliver services; the importance of training and high standards for both volunteers and paid professionals; concerns about vulnerability and being 'bullied' into colluding with low standards (e.g. signing for home care which should last for one hour but only lasts 15 minutes).

Geriatrics

Please do not use this term. No geriatric beds, no mixed wards either.

Not being valued

Powerful messages about the experiences and the time of elderly people not being valued; services seen as scheduled for the benefit of professionals rather than patients.

Discharge from hospital

Discharge from hospital is successfully managed for only a minority of patients. Getting patients to and from outpatient departments and accident and emergency units matters just as much as planned discharge from hospital beds, but is rarely done well.

Modest demands

The health service is not good at simple things (e.g. putting people in a mini-cab or providing telephones). The system seems to be better at dealing with complex cases than straightforward ones.

Local workshops

In October and November, we worked with the health and social care agencies in four localities to understand more about the barriers to change. The localities were Canning Town, Redbridge, Dulwich and Croydon. They were selected because we knew that they were working to improve services for elderly people; were prepared to involve people from several agencies in the workshops; and were able to meet our phase 1 deadline of November.

The four levels consisted of the following.

- *A neighbourhood.* Elderly people and their carers in Canning Town together with their local professionals, a general practitioner, district nurse, health visitor, voluntary groups, and occupational therapists.
- *A general practice population.* A large general practice in Dulwich who brought nurses from the community trust, the discharge planner from the local hospital, a local pharmacist and a 'home-from-hospital' private agency.
- *Operational management.* Managers from the hospital and community health services in Redbridge, who brought the local authority community, care planner, the voluntary organisations coordinator, and development managers from the health authorities.
- *Policy level.* Senior executives in Croydon from the local authority, social services, environmental health and housing, the health commission, the local hospital, a GP, community groups, the community health services trust, the mental health trust.

Each workshop brought together people already working to provide services for elderly people in their patch. Because these are often vulnerable people, the system of care is complex and involves many different agencies and professionals. It was this complexity that we wanted to understand.

In Redbridge, for example, we traced the progress of a hypothetical elderly person with a minor stroke being taken to the Accident and Emergency department at 10pm. It gradually became clear that most bits of the system know little about the reality of other bits and that often what appears to be a solution in one place merely shifts the burden. Often this happens in ways which are unanticipated and counterproductive.

In Canning Town and in Dulwich, everyone was agreed on the importance of mobility and transport – whether by mini-cab, ambulance or an 'arm to lean on' and yet transport was seen to be quite disconnected from other parts of the system.

Much of what comes out of these workshops echoes the London-wide meetings and confirms that users are key to understanding the experience of the system. What we learned from these events is that if the right people are brought together, they can gain a much clearer understanding of the 'big picture', and move beyond simplistic, short-term assumptions about cause and effect.

Other cities

Other cities face similar issues to London. We have therefore tested our London experience with colleagues from Liverpool, Sheffield, Newcastle, Birmingham, and Manchester who meet at the King's Fund as an Urban Primary Care Network. The people involved come from general practice, health authorities, universities, community health councils, community health providers, regional health authorities and the NHS Executive. They are key players in developing the community-based health services which are underdeveloped in our cities and on which much attention is now focused. Their experience confirms the London fieldwork:

- it is difficult to use one-off, time-limited money well.
- short timescale project bidding should be avoided and new ways of working should be developed.
- anything which helps the health and social care system understand itself as a whole, is likely to lead to better judgements about using development money to bring about lasting change.
- cities face distinctive problems which are not the same as other parts of the country.

Next steps

Many of the problems in primary care result from the complexity of our health and social care system. This chimes with common sense and yet it is notoriously difficult for agencies working together to see 'the big picture'. Without this, the solutions to problems often turn out to be 'sticking plaster solutions' with knock-on effects, which are seldom anticipated. Time-limited project money is often offered and used in this way but seldom brings about the desired lasting change.

The work we have done so far suggests that intractable problems can be addressed constructively. Over the next few months we will continue to work in a few localities to test whether adopting a 'whole-system approach' leads to clearer judgements about the action needed to improve services.

The Partnership is not a research programme. The commitment to action is crucial. The people we will work with are already thinking about different ways of delivering services and of doing better with the resources they have.

December 1994.

References

1. Acheson D. *Primary Healthcare in Inner London*. London Health Planning Consortium 1981.

2. Hughes J, Gordon P. *An Optimal Balance: Primary Healthcare and Acute Hospital Services in London*. London: King's Fund, 1992.

3. Nicholas R M. *Making London Better – the clearing house and ring-fencing scheme: extension of the ring fencing and vacancy notification criteria*. Leeds, Department of Health, 1994.

4. Turnberg L. *Health Services in London – A Strategic Review*. London Department of Health, 1998.

5. Pratt J. *Understanding the Boundaries of Primary Care, in Extending Primary Care* eds Gordon & Hadley. Oxford: Radcliffe,1996.

6. Shien E. H. *Process Consultation Vol.1*. Addison Wesley, 1988.

7. Norman R, Ramirez R. *Designing Interactive Strategy: from value chain to value constillation*. Chichester: Wiley, 1994.

8. Lukes S.(ed) *Power* (Reading in Social & Political Thoery 4) New York University Press, 1996.

9. Sibbet D et al. *The Graphic Guide to Facilitation Principles/Practice*, Version 1, San Francisco: Graphic Guides Inc, March 1993.

10. Checkland P. *Systems Thinking Systems Practice*. Chichester: Wiley, 1981.

11. Forrester J. *Industrial Dynamics: a major break-through for decision-making*. Harvard Buisness Review. Cambridge, Massachusetts : Vol.36, no 4 1958.

12. Stacey R D. *Strategic Management and Organisational Dynamics*. London: Pitman, 1996.

13. Senge P M et al. *The Fifth Discipline: the art and practice of the learning organisation*. London: Century Business, 1990.

14. Wardman K J, Cornell C. *The Toolbox Reprint Service*: Systems Archetypes Pegasus Communications, 1996

15. Wheatley M. *Leadership and the New Science*. San Francisco: Brett-Koehler, 1992.

16. Van Gundy A B. *Techniques of Structured Problem Solving*. New York: Workingham Van Nostrand Reinhold, 1988.

17. Ackoff B. *The Future Of Operational Research Is Past*: Journal of Operational Research. Birmingham Society of Operational Research 1979.

18. Rittel, Weber. *Dilemmas in a General Theory of Planning*. Policy Science, New York: 4. 1973.

19. Pava L. *New Strategies for Systems Change: Reclaiming Nonsynoptic Methods*. Human Relations Vol. 39, No.7. Plenum Press, 1986.

20. Jacobs J. *Death and life of Great American Cities* London: Penguin, 1994.

21. Henry J, Walker D. *Managing Innovation*. Newbury Park: Sage, 1991.

22. Harris J, Gordon P. et al. *Projectitis: Spending money and the trouble with project bidding*. Whole Systems Thinking Series, London. King's Fund 1998.

23. Shon D. *Champions of Radical New Inventions*. Harvard Buisness Review, March – April 1963.

24. McMaster M D. *The Intelligence Advantage: organising for complexity*. The Knowledge Based Development Company, Douglas: Isle of Man 1995.

25. Lewin K. *Research on Minority Problems*. Technology Review, 48(3).1946

26. Casti J L. *Complexification: explaining a paradoxical world through the science of surprise*. London: Abacus, 1994.

27. Prigogine I, Stengers I. *Order Out of Chaos: Man's new dialogue with nature*. London: Flamingo, 1995.

28. Lovelock JE. *Gaia: A New Look at Life on Earth*. Oxford University Press 1987.

29. Maturana V. *The Tree of Knowledge*. Boston: Shambhala Publishing Inc, 1996.

30. Bunker B B, Alban B T. *The Journal of Applied Behavioural Science*. Vol.28, No.4. Newbury Park: Sage, 1992.

31. Weisbord M R, Janoff S. *Future Search: an action guide to finding common ground in organizations and communities*. San Francisco Brett-Kohler, 1995.

32. Owen H. *Open Space Technology: a user's guide*. Potomac: Abbott Publishing, 1992.

33. Working Paper Series: *Whole System Thinking*. London: King's Fund 1998.

   Projectitis: John Harries, Pat Gordon, Diane Plamping and Martin Fischer.

   Partnership fit for purpose: Julian Pratt, Diane Plamping and Pat Gordon.

   Action Zones and Large Numbers: Diane Plamping, Julian Pratt and Pat Gordon.

   Creative Writing: Margaret Wilkinson.

34. Pratt J, Plamping D, and Gordon P. *Working Whole Systems: practice and theory in network organisations*. London: King's Fund (in press).

Projectitis:

Spending lots of money and the trouble with project bidding

John Harries, Pat Gordon, Diane Plamping and Martin Fischer

Why does short-term investment in one-off projects seldom deliver the desired outcomes for organisational change? Why does the learning from demonstration projects seldom transfer to other places? This paper considers these conundrums and offers a different way of thinking about how to use development resources.

Price £5.00
ISBN 1 85717 211 6

Action Zones and Large Numbers:

Why working with lots of people makes sense

Diane Plamping, Pat Gordon and Julian Pratt

Action zones will have to find ways of engaging the energy and commitment of large numbers of people. If they are to 'break the mould' and deliver fundamental change, they will have to find genuinely new ways of working. This paper suggests a way of productively involving large numbers of people at every stage.

Price £5.00
ISBN 1 85717 226 4

Creative Writing:

Its role in evaluation

Margaret Wilkinson

Creative writing can provide a powerful tool in qualitative evaluation. The exercises and examples in this book are based on writing games, story telling and memory. They are affirming, problem-solving and democratising. Evaluation becomes something that everyone is asked to think about and take part in.

Price £5.00
ISBN 1 85717 228 0

Partnership: Fit for purpose?

Julian Pratt, Diane Plamping, Pat Gordon

Partnership between organisations is hard to achieve. There is often a mismatch between our aspirations for partnership and the frustration of our experience in practice. This paper offers a way of thinking about the purpose of partnership; partnership behaviours which fit different purposes; and partnership behaviours which can lead to sustainable change and are not dependant on injections of external resources.

Price £5.00
ISBN 1 85717 229 9

Coming soon . . .

Working Whole Systems

Julian Pratt, Pat Gordon and Diane Plamping

This book brings together the various strands of our thinking and practice and describes our approach to whole system working.

All titles in the Whole Systems Thinking series are available from:

King's Fund Bookshop, 11–13 Cavendish Square, London W1M 0AN
Tel: 0171 307 2591 Fax: 0171 307 2801